# Rudolph's
# Riddles

*Rudolph's Riddles*
*Published by IOM Press in 2018.*
*www.iompress.org*

*ISBN : 978-1-9164076-2-6*

What am I? ...................................................... 1

Lateral thinking puzzles ........................................ 27

How do you explain that? ....................................... 43

Quick-fire round ............................................... 71

Answers ........................................................ 88

what
am I?

I am an odd number. Remove one letter and I become even. What am I?

I am always with you, but am often left behind. What am I?

Sometimes long, and sometimes short, I have two ends but no beginning. What am I?

I am black when clean
and white when dirty.
What am I?

I always end everything.
What am I?

I have hands that move
but I cannot clap.
What am I?

I am not alive but
I can die.
What am I?

I am always in front of you,
but yet I am never here.
What am I?

I have an eye, but
never cry.
What am I?

I start with a P and
end with an X. I have a
never-ending amount of letters.
What am I?

Once you have me, you want to
share me. Once you share me,
you no longer have me.
What am I?

I can go up a chimney down, but
can't go down a chimey up.
What am I?

5

The more you take out of me,
the bigger I become.
What am I?

I'm always somewhere between
the ground and the sky, always
far in the distance, always moving
further away if one attempts to
come closer.
What am I?

Feed me, and I will thrive.
But give me a drink and
I will die.
What am I?

6

You hear me once, then
you hear me again.
Then I die, until you
call me again.
What am I?

I'm tall when I'm young
and I'm short when I'm old.
What am I?

I go up but never down.
What am I?

I start with a T, end with a T,
and am full of T.
What am I?

I turn everything around but
cannot move.
What am I?

I can be made, laid down,
bent and broken, but am difficult
to touch.
What am I?

8

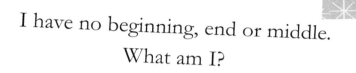

I have no beginning, end or middle.
What am I?

You use me between your head
and your toes. The more you use
me the thinner I grow.
What am I?

I go up and down, towards the
sky and ground. I'm present and
past tense too. Let's go for a ride,
me and you.
What am I?

I have an eye but cannot see.
I am fast but I have no limbs.
What am I?

I can be measured but
never seen. What am I?

I can only be used
when broken.
What am I?

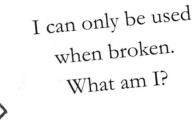

Poor people have me,
rich people need me.
If you eat me you will die.
What am I?

I can run around a house
but never move.
What am I?

Say my name and I disappear.
What am I?

I exist in life but not in death.
You can't have fun without me.
What am I?

I run but never walk, have a
bed but never sleep, and
have a mouth but never eat.
What am I?

I turn around once.
What is out will not get in.
I turn around again.
What is in will not get out.
What am I?

I get wet as soon as I am
left out in the sun.
What am I?

At night I come without being
fetched. By day I am lost
without being stolen.
What am I?

It's the only organ in the human
body that gave itself its own
name.
What is it?

I can be seen once in a minute,
twice in a moment, but never
in a thousand years.
What am I?

I have a head but no body,
though I do have a tail.
What am I?

I can fill a room but take up
no space.
What am I?

The more you take the
more you leave behind.
What am I?

Sometimes I walk in front of you.
Sometimes I walk behind you. It
is only in the dark that I will ever
leave you.
What am I?

You buy me to eat, and
yet never eat me.
What am I?

I shave everyday but my
beard always stays the same.
Who am I?

I contain five letters, which you'll
find in a tennis court.
What am I?

I'm always hungry and must be fed.
The finger that touches me
will soon turn red.
What am I?

16

Sometimes I am light,
sometimes I am dark.
Most people like me.
What am I?

I move without legs
and cry without eyes.
What am I?

You bury me when I'm alive and
dig me up when I'm dead.
What am I?

17

Forward I'm heavy, but
backwards I'm not.
What am I?

I exist only when there is light,
but direct light kills me.
What am I?

You throw me out
when you need me most,
but put me away
when you don't.
What am I?

If you look in water, you will
likely see me. And yet I
never get wet.
What am I?

I travel all over the world, but
always stay in my corner.
What am I?

I get wetter the more I dry.
What am I?

I have many keys but cannot open a single lock.
What am I?

I have one head, one foot and four legs.
What am I?

Most people need me, some ask for me, but many choose not to listen to me.
What am I?

When I take five and add six,
I get eleven. But when I take six
and add seven, I get one.
What am I?

I have a soul but no heart,
and a tongue but I can't taste.
What am I?

I am in seasons, seconds,
centuries and minutes, but not in
decades, years or days.
What am I?

I am always on my way,
but never arrive.
What am I?

I run downhill but
never walk.
What am I?

I no longer have eyes,
but once I could see.
Once I had thoughts,
but now I'm empty.
What am I?

22

I can be served but
cannot be eaten.
What am I?

You answer me, but I
never ask you a question.
What am I?

I have 13 hearts but no lungs
or other organs.
What am I?

I have six faces and
twenty-one eyes.
What am I?

I have five fingers but
have never lived.
What am I?

I can hold lots of water
but am full of holes.
What am I?

I have cities but no houses.
I have mountains but no trees.
I have water but no fish.
What am I?

The more you have of me,
the less you see.
What am I?

You can you see in the middle
of March and April but not at
the beginning or end of either
month.
What am I?

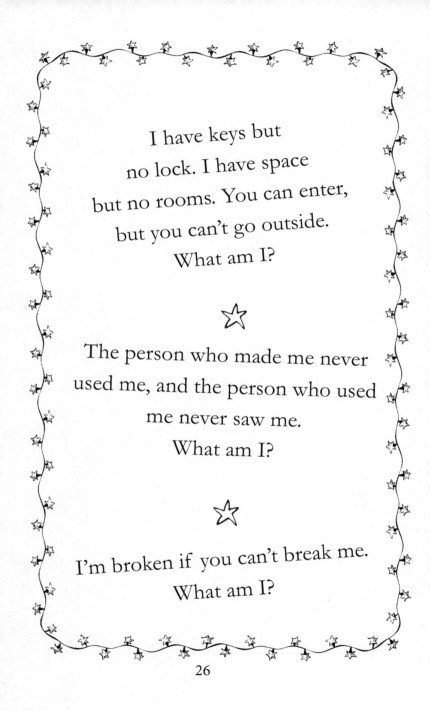

I have keys but
no lock. I have space
but no rooms. You can enter,
but you can't go outside.
What am I?

The person who made me never
used me, and the person who used
me never saw me.
What am I?

I'm broken if you can't break me.
What am I?

Lateral
thinking
puzzles

What is something you will never see again, no matter how hard you try to make it happen?

What gets harder to catch the faster you run?

What occurs once in a year, twice in a week, but never in a day?

What tastes better
than it smells?

What can you hold in
your right hand, but
never in your left hand?

If you are running in a race and
pass the person in second place,
what place are you in now?

What English word has
three consecutive
double letters?

What do the numbers
11, 69, 88 and 96
all have in common?

Two Indians are standing on a
bridge. One is the father of the
other's son. What is
the relationship
between them?

How can a person go
eight days without sleep?

What word contains
all 26 letters?

You walk a mile south, a mile
east, and then a mile north.
You end up in exactly the same
spot where you started.
Where are you?

31

What question can you ask someone, where you get a different answer every time, but all the answers are correct?

Name a building you can leave without ever having entered.

In what month do people sleep the least?

32

What word becomes
shorter when you
add two letters to it?

When does yesterday
come after today?

You are my sister but
I am not your sister.
Who am I?

A man looks out of a window. He longs to open it, but knows it would kill him if he did. Why?

What can be larger than you without weighing anything?

If I stand on top of a hill and ring a loud bell between two houses, which house will hear the bell first - the one to the west, or the one to the east?

How many eggs can you put into an empty basket?

⭐

A barrel of water weighs 75kg. What must you add to it to make it 50kg?

⭐

What English word sounds the same even after you take away four of its five letters?

⭐

What falls but does not
break, and what breaks
but does not fall?

I know a word of letters three.
Add two more and fewer
there will be.
What is the word?

What is lighter than a feather,
but can't be held for long
by even the world's
strongest man?

Which tyre doesn't
move when a car
turns right?

What question can
you never honestly
say "yes" to?

Who gets paid to drive away
their customers?

37

A car departs London at the same time as a lorry leaves Edinburgh. The car travels at 70mph on average, while the lorry travels at just 40mph. Which is the furthest away from London when they meet?

What times starts and stops with an "n"?

When can you add 2 to 11 and get 1 as the answer?

What kind of paint can
you only put on
when it's wet?

What belongs to you
but is used by everyone
you meet?

Which month has 28 days?

"I've got 10 or more sisters."
"I've got fewer than 10 sisters."
"I've got at least one sister."
If only one of these statements
is true, how many sisters
have I got?

What instrument can you
hear but never see?

What is at the end of
every rainbow?

What man has married many women but never had a wife?

What makes you young?

Who do you see everyday but don't know?

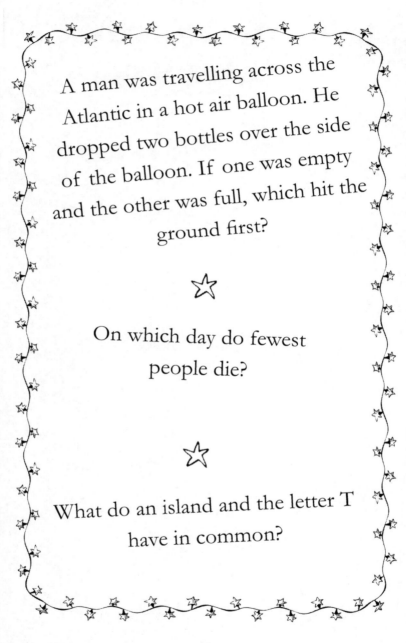

A man was travelling across the Atlantic in a hot air balloon. He dropped two bottles over the side of the balloon. If one was empty and the other was full, which hit the ground first?

☆

On which day do fewest people die?

☆

What do an island and the letter T have in common?

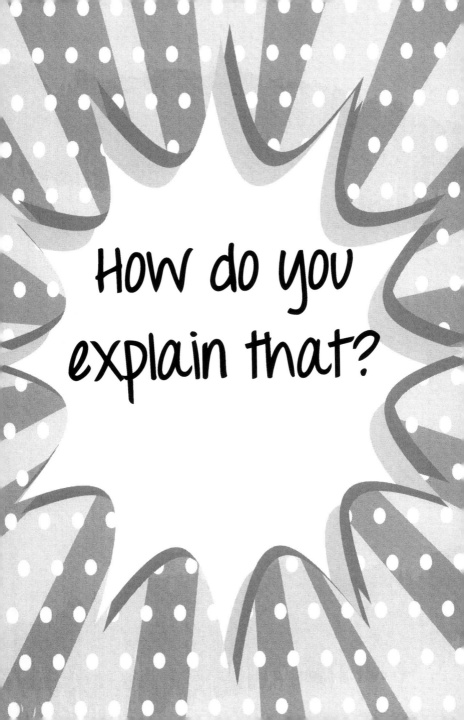

Tom is the father of Charlie, but Charlie is not the son of Tom. How is this possible?

A woman goes to the police station late at night and destroys large numbers of fingerprints. Despite the fact that she is caught doing this on camera, the police do not arrest her. Why not?

A bus driver goes the wrong
way down a one-way street.
He passes the police,
but they don't stop him.
Why?

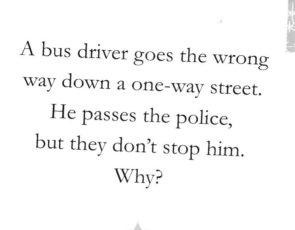

An archaeologist digs up two
perfectly preserved bodies. He
immediately identifies them as
Adam and Eve.
How can he be so sure?

A man lies dead in a field.
There is no other living thing
in the field with him,
but next to him lies an
unopened package.
How did he die?

I bumped into my long-lost
uncle in the street. I'd never
met him, seen his picture,
or heard him described before,
and yet I recognised
him instantly.
How?

A man stopped
his car opposite a hotel
and immediately knew he
was bankrupt. How?

A woman was having
breakfast in a restaurant when she
suddenly noticed a fly in her coffee.
She asked the waiter to bring
her a new cup.
After he returned with her coffee,
she became angry and shouted,
"How dare you. You have
brought me the same
cup of coffee!"
How did she know?

47

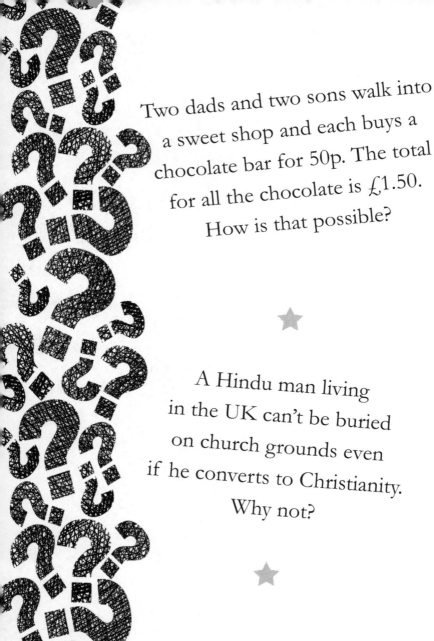

Two dads and two sons walk into a sweet shop and each buys a chocolate bar for 50p. The total for all the chocolate is £1.50. How is that possible?

A Hindu man living in the UK can't be buried on church grounds even if he converts to Christianity. Why not?

Two girls were born to the
same mother, on the same
day, at the same time, in the
same month and year,
and yet they're not twins.
How can this be?

A boy and his father are in
a car crash. The father dies
and the boy is rushed
to hospital. The surgeon sees
the boy and says,
"I can't operate on him,
he's my son!"
How can this be?

Mary was born on December 25th, yet her birthday is always in the summer. How is this possible?

A man leaves hospital and begins to walk home. On his journey, he passes a phonebox, which begins to ring. Instead of answering it, he punches the air and runs all the way home cheering. Why?

At a family reunion,
one man went up to
another and said, "Father!"
"Grandad!" replied the other.
Neither was mistaken.
Explain.

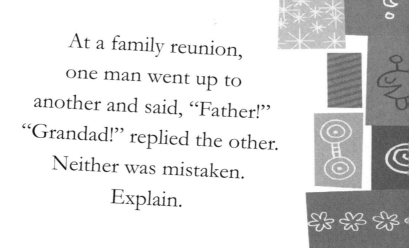

Two men are playing chess.
They play five games.
Each man wins three games.
How is that possible?

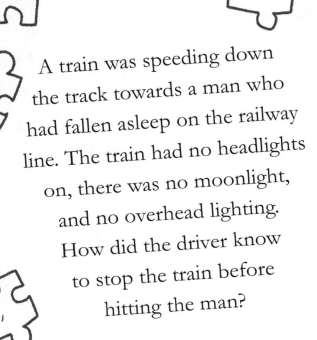

A train was speeding down
the track towards a man who
had fallen asleep on the railway
line. The train had no headlights
on, there was no moonlight,
and no overhead lighting.
How did the driver know
to stop the train before
hitting the man?

A cowboy rides into town on
Friday, stays for three days
and leaves on Friday.
How is this possible?

A doctor and a bus driver
are both in love with the same
woman. The bus driver has
to go away for a week. Before
he leaves, he gives the
woman seven apples.
Why?

A man went into a bar and asked
the barman for a glass of water.
The barman pointed a gun at
him. The man thanked
the barman and left.
Why?

One day, a man jumped from a plane without a parachute and suffered no injuries.
How is that possible?

A man was stabbed in the heart. Nobody tried to save him, and yet he didn't die.
Can you explain why?

A boy throws a tennis ball. It travels 1 metre and then goes right back to the boy.
How is that possible?

An engineer and a 10-year-old boy go fishing. The boy was the engineer's son, but the engineer wasn't the boy's dad. How do you explain this?

A town has only to barbers. One of the barbers has a nice tidy haircut and the other has a messy, shaggy haircut. Despite this, most people prefer to go to the barber with the messy hair. Why?

There is a dog on one side of a lake and a woman on the other. The woman calls the dog, who swiftly crosses the lake. But when he greets the woman, he is not wet at all.

Can you explain this?

★

If a cat can jump 3 metres high, why can't it jump through a window that is only 2 metres off the ground?

A lorry attempted to drive under a low bridge but it got stuck. People stopped and tried to help the driver free the vehicle, but they couldn't push it either forwards or backwards. How did they eventually free the lorry?

How can you take two away from five and be left with four?

Mr Jones wanted a house
where the windows in
all the rooms faced south.
How did he manage this?

A man set out on a
journey and stopped only
when he returned to his
starting point. During that journey,
his head travelled 12½ metres
further than his feet, yet
his feet remained attached
to his body.
Can you
explain this?

58

Every morning a woman takes the lift from her flat on the 12th floor down to the ground floor, leaves the building and goes to work. When she returns in the evening, however, she always gets out of the lift on the 8th floor and walks up the remaining 4 flights of stairs to her flat. She is not a keep-fit fanatic, so why does she do this?

Two friends were drinking iced tea in a coffee shop. One of the girls was very thirsty and drank 5 glasses of iced tea in quick succession. The other girl was less thirsty and sipped her drink, making it last the full hour they were together. Tragically, the girl who had only one drink died, while the other suffered no ill consequences. When the police analysed the cups, they found traces of poison in all six glasses. How come only one of the girls died?

A man was cleaning the windows of a four-storey building. He slipped and fell off the ladder, but wasn't hurt. How is that possible?

A man was murdered in his office. The numbers 6, 4, 9, 10 and 11 are written on the calendar in blood.
The police identify five suspects, namely Gerry, Julie, Jason, Nick and Sophie. Who do you think is the killer and why?

A woman was just about to go to bed, when a man burst into her room and pointed a gun at her. Just then, the phone rang. The intruder instructed the woman to answer the phone, and tell the caller that she would phone them back later. The woman did as she was told, and said the following: "Hi mum, do you need help with something? I'm really tired and just about to go to bed. If it's not an emergency, can I call you later please?" A few minutes later, the police arrived and arrested the man. How did the woman's mum know to phone the police?

A man is found hanging
in a barn from a central rafter,
with a wet patch underneath him.
The rope around his neck is
2 metres long, and his feet are
1 metre off the ground. The walls
are 5 metres away. There is
nothing else in the building,
no ladders or boxes or chairs.
How did the man manage to
hang himself?

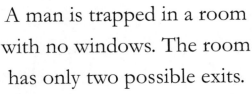

A man is trapped in a room with no windows. The room has only two possible exits. Through the first door there is a giant magnifying glass that magnifies the light from the sun, instantly frying anything or anyone that enters. Through the second door, there is a fire-breathing dragon.
Can you work out how the man escapes?

A man was found shot to
death in his car. The police
find no traces of gunpowder
on his clothes or in his car,
which they say means he was
shot by someone outside of
his car. The car doors were
locked and the windows
were shut, and there
were no bullet holes
in the car.
How is this possible?

A man is cleaning windows on the 40th floor of a skyscraper. Despite his wife constantly nagging him to wear a harness, he doesn't have one on. He slips on some soap suds and falls to the ground. A few minutes later he gets up, dusts himself off and returns to his cleaning. Can you explain why the window cleaner wasn't injured?

My favourite team has won seven times this season, but they haven't scored a single goal. Explain.

A woman was staying in a hotel room. Suddenly there was a knock on the door. She opened the door and saw a man standing there. He looked surprised and apologised, saying, "I'm sorry, I thought it was my room."
He walked off in the direction of the lifts. The woman closed the door and called hotel security.
Why was she so suspicious?

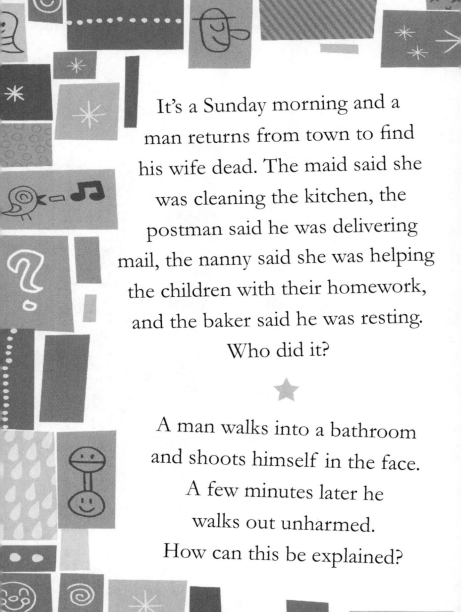

It's a Sunday morning and a man returns from town to find his wife dead. The maid said she was cleaning the kitchen, the postman said he was delivering mail, the nanny said she was helping the children with their homework, and the baker said he was resting. Who did it?

A man walks into a bathroom and shoots himself in the face. A few minutes later he walks out unharmed. How can this be explained?

68

A girl goes to her mother's funeral and meets the man of her dreams, but she doesn't get his name or number. Three days later, the girl kills her own sister. Why?

A man went to bed but couldn't fall asleep. He reached for his phone, called someone, but hung up after a few rings without saying anything, and promptly fell asleep. Who did he call and why?

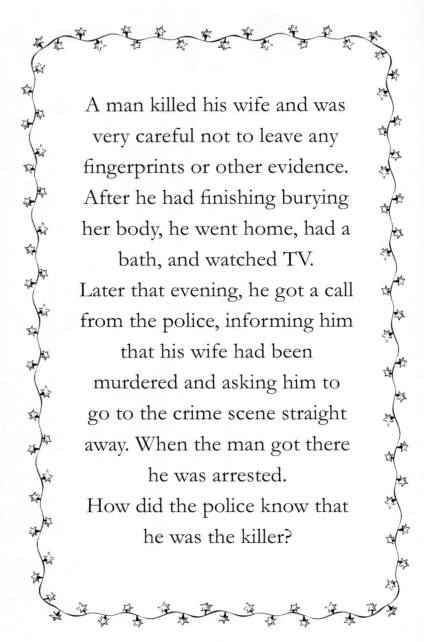

A man killed his wife and was very careful not to leave any fingerprints or other evidence. After he had finishing burying her body, he went home, had a bath, and watched TV.
Later that evening, he got a call from the police, informing him that his wife had been murdered and asking him to go to the crime scene straight away. When the man got there he was arrested.
How did the police know that he was the killer?

Quick-fire
round

How many animals of each species did Moses take on the ark with him?

⭐

Say the following: roast, boast, coast, post.
What do you put in a toaster?

⭐

Which word is written incorrectly in the dictionary?

72

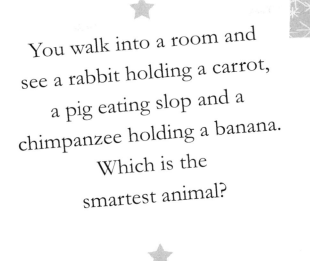

You walk into a room and see a rabbit holding a carrot, a pig eating slop and a chimpanzee holding a banana. Which is the smartest animal?

If one man can dig one hole in two days, how long will it take two men to dig half a hole?

# CHALLENGE

The following maths equation is **not** correct.
Can you add one **straight** line to it to make it true?

$$5 + 5 + 5 = 550$$

# What's wrong with this picture?

At midnight, it is
raining hard.
How likely is it that it
will be sunny in
72 hours?

How do you spell
hard water with only
three letters?

Why can't someone
living in Edinburgh
be buried
in London?

76

First think of the
colour of the clouds.
Next think of the
colour of snow.
Now think of the
colour of the moon.
Answer quickly:
what do cows drink?

What is the mistake
in the the following list?
A, B, C, D, E, F, G, H, I, J,
K, L, M, N, O, P, Q, R
S, T, U, V, W, X, Y, Z

# CHALLENGE

Remove SIX matches

to make TEN

# What's wrong with this picture?

Imagine you are in a
sinking boat and
surrounded by sharks.
What could you do
to survive?

If an electric train is
travelling west at
90 miles per hour and there
is a strong easterly wind,
which way would the
smoke from the train drift?

If an electric train is
travelling west at
90 miles per hour and there
is a strong easterly wind,
which way would the
smoke from the train drift?

A rooster laid an egg
on top of a barn.
Which way did it fall?

What word looks the same
upside down and
backwards?

What mathematical symbol
can you put between
2 and 3 to make a number
greater than 2 but
less than 3?

Can you name three
consecutive days without
using Sunday, Wednesday
and Friday?

What do you get when you multiply all the numbers on a telephone keypad together?

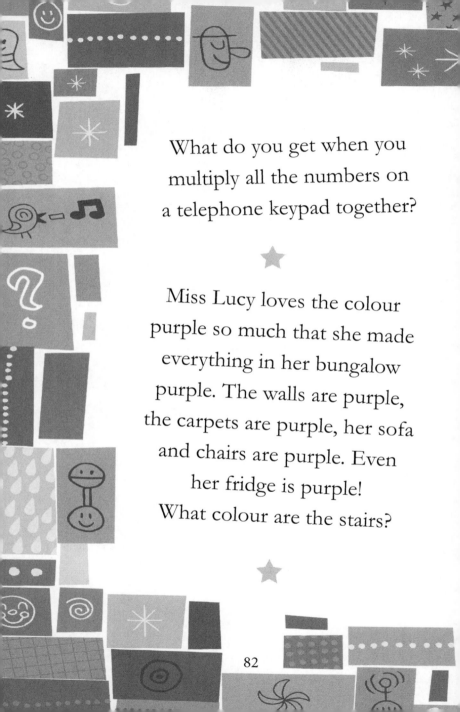

Miss Lucy loves the colour purple so much that she made everything in her bungalow purple. The walls are purple, the carpets are purple, her sofa and chairs are purple. Even her fridge is purple! What colour are the stairs?

What are the next three
letters in this combination:
O T T F F S?

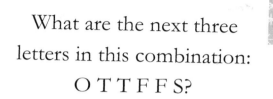

2 coins add up to 3 pence.
One of them is not a
2 pence coin.
What are the coins?

Mary's mother has 3 daughters.
The first as called April, and the
second is named May.
What is the name of the
third daughter?

Without using the number 4,
can you come up with
a simple addition sum using
three identical digits,
so that the answer is 12?

What can you add to the
number one to
make it disappear?

Railroad crossing,
watch out for the cars.
How do you spell that
without any Rs?

What happened in
Germany on
June 31st, 1945?

What weighs more,
a kilogram of feathers,
or a kilogram of bricks?

If something funny is a joke,
and people can be called folk,
what do you call
the white of an egg

85

There are 7 birds in a tree.
A hunter shoots one bird down.
How many birds are
left in the tree?

☆

A plane crashes directly on the
border of France and Germany.
Where do they
bury the survivors?

☆

A man is in his car. He sees
3 doors: a golden one,
a diamond one, and a silver one.
Which door does he
go through first?

# ALSO AVAILABLE

If you enjoyed this book, you might also like Ho Ho Ho! Santa's Christmas Joke Book, available from Amazon.

# ANSWERS (WHAT AM I?)

**Page 2**
  **Top:** Seven
  **Middle:** Fingerprints
  **Bottom:** A piece of string

**Page 3**
  **Top:** A blackboard
  **Middle:** The letter g
  **Bottom:** A clock

**Page 4**
  **Top:** A battery
  **Middle:** The future
  **Bottom:** A needle

**Page 5**
  **Top:** A postbox
  **Middle:** A secret
  **Bottom:** An umbrella

**Page 6**
  **Top:** A hole or pit
  **Middle:** The horizon
  **Bottom:** Fire

**Page 7**
  **Top:** An echo
  **Middle:** A candle
  **Bottom:** Our age

**Page 8**
  **Top:** A teapot
  **Middle:** Mirror
  **Bottom:** Rules

**Page 9**
  **Top:** A doughnut
  **Middle:** A bar of soap
  **Bottom:** A See Saw

**Page 10**
  **Top:** A hurricane
  **Middle:** Time
  **Bottom:** An egg

**Page 11**
  **Top:** Nothing
  **Middle:** A fence
  **Bottom:** Silence

**Page 12**
  **Top:** The letter f
  **Middle:** A river
  **Bottom:** A key

**Page 13**
  **Top:** Ice
  **Middle:** Stars
  **Bottom:** The brain

**Page 14**
  **Top:** The letter m
  **Middle:** A coin
  **Bottom:** Light

**Page 15**
  **Top:** Footsteps
  **Middle:** Your shadow
  **Bottom:** Cutlery

**Page 16**
   **Top:** A barber
   **Middle:** Vowels (a, i, e, o, u)
   **Bottom:** Fire

**Page 17**
   **Top:** Chocolate
   **Middle:** A cloud
   **Bottom:** A plant

**Page 18**
   **Top:** Ton (not backwards)
   **Middle:** A shadow
   **Bottom:** An anchor

**Page 19**
   **Top:** A reflection
   **Middle:** A stamp
   **Bottom:** A towel

**Page 20**
   **Top:** A piano
   **Middle:** A bed
   **Bottom:** Advice

**Page 21**
   **Top:** A clock
   **Middle:** A shoe
   **Bottom:** The letter n

**Page 22**
   **Top:** Tomorrow
   **Middle:** Water
   **Bottom:** A skull

**Page 23**
   **Top:** A tennis ball
   **Middle:** A telephone
   **Bottom:** A deck of cards

**Page 24**
   **Top:** A dice
   **Middle:** A glove
   **Bottom:** A sponge

**Page 25**
   **Top:** A map
   **Middle:** Darkness
   **Bottom:** The letter r

**Page 26**
   **Top:** A computer keyboard
   **Middle:** A coffin
   **Bottom:** A piñata

# ANSWERS (LATERAL THINKING PUZZLES)

**Page 28**
 **Top:** Yesterday
 **Middle:** Your breath
 **Bottom:** The letter e

**Page 29**
 Top: Your tongue
 Middle: Your left hand
 Bottom: Second place

**Page 30**
 **Top:** Bookkeeper
 **Middle:** They are the same upside down
 **Bottom:** Husband and wife

**Page 31**
 **Top:** By sleeping at night
 **Middle:** Alphabet
 **Bottom:** The North Pole

**Page 32**
 **Top:** What time is it?
 **Middle:** The hospital you were born in
 **Bottom:** February, as it has the fewest number of days

**Page 33**
 **Top:** Short
 **Middle:** In the dictionary
 **Bottom:** Your brother

**Page 34**
 **Top:** He's in a submarine under the sea
 **Middle:** Your shadow
 **Bottom:** Neither - houses can't hear!

**Page 35**
 **Top:** One - after this the basket won't be empty
 **Middle:** Holes
 **Bottom:** Queue

**Page 36**
 **Top:** Night falls and day breaks
 **Middle:** Few
 **Bottom:** Your breath

**Page 37**
 **Top:** The spare tyre
 **Middle:** "Are you asleep?"
 **Bottom:** Taxi drivers

**Page 38**
 **Top:** Neither. They are the same distance away
 **Middle:** Noon
 **Bottom:** When you're looking at a clock (Add two hours to 11 o'clock to get 1 o'clock)

**Page 39**
   **Top:** A coat of paint
   **Middle:** Your name
   **Bottom:** All of them

**Page 40**
   **Top:** None. If "I've got at
   least one sister" is true, then
   either "I've got fewer than
   10 sisters" or "I've got 10 or
   more sisters" must be true.
   "I've got fewer than 10
   sisters" can be true by itself,
   but only if I have no sisters
   **Middle:** Your voice
   **Bottom:** The letter w

**Page 41**
   **Top:** A priest
   **Middle:** Adding the letters
   ng, which turns "you" into
   "young"
   **Bottom:** Strangers

**Page 42**
   **Top:** Since the man was
   flying over the sea, neither
   bottle hit the ground
   **Middle:** February 29th
   **Bottom:** They are both in the
   middle of water

## ANSWERS (HOW DO YOU EXPLAIN THAT?)

**Page 44**
    **Top:** Charlie is a girl
    **Bottom:** The woman is the
    police station cleaner

**Page 45**
    **Top:** He was walking
    **Bottom:** They have no
    belly buttons as they
    weren't born from another
    human being

**Page 46**
    **Top:** He was doing
    a parachute jump. The
    package next to him is his
    parachute, which failed to
    open, causing the man to
    fall to his death
    **Bottom:** He is my dad's
    identical twin brother

**Page 47**
    **Top:** It was a game of
    monopoly
    **Bottom:** She had already
    stirred sugar into her
    coffee. When she tasted
    the new coffee, it was
    sweet, suggesting that the
    waiter had brought her
    back the same cup

**Page 48**
    **Top:** There were only
    three men, a grandfather,
    a father and a son
    **Bottom:** You can't bury
    the living

**Page 49**
    **Top:** They are part of a
    set of triplets
    **Bottom:** The surgeon is
    the boy's mum

**Page 50**
    **Top:** She lives in the
    southern hemisphere
    **Bottom:** The man had an
    operation in hospital to
    cure his deafness, and the
    fact that he could hear the
    telephone ringing showed
    that the operation had
    been a success

**Page 51**
    **Top:** The grandson was
    a priest
    **Bottom:** They weren't
    playing each other

### Page 52

**Top:** It was daytime, so the driver was able to see the man

**Bottom:** The cowboy's horse was called Friday

### Page 53

**Top:** The bus driver heard the proverb, 'An apple a day keeps the doctor away!' and thought that he would try it out

**Bottom:** The man had hiccups, so the barman pointed a gun at him to scare the hiccups away

### Page 54

**Top:** The plane was on the ground

**Middle:** He was already dead

**Bottom:** The boy threw the ball straight up in the air

### Page 55

**Top:** The engineer was the boy's mum

**Bottom:** The barbers cut each other's hair

### Page 56

**Top:** The lake is frozen

**Bottom:** Because the window is closed

### Page 57

**Top:** They let some air out of the tyres to reduce the height of the lorry

**Bottom:** Take the letters F and E off the word FIVE. This leaves you with IV, which is four in Roman numerals.

### Page 58

**Top:** He built his house at the North Pole, which meant that every wall faced south

**Bottom:** The journey was around the globe. The man's head was around 2 metres from the ground, which means that the circumference of the circle travelled by his head is greater than that of the circle travelled by his feet. Using the formula for the circumference of a circle, we can work out that his head travelled $2\pi \times 2 = 12.57$m further than his feet

# ANSWERS (HOW DO YOU EXPLAIN THAT?)

### Page 59

The woman is too short to reach the 12th floor button in the lift

### Page 60

The poison was contained in the ice. The girl who survived drank her drinks quickly, before the ice melted and released the poison into the tea

### Page 61

**Top:** He fell off the bottom rung of the ladder
**Bottom:** Jason is the killer. The numbers on the calendar correspond to the months June, April, September, October and November, spelling out Jason

### Page 62

The woman pressed the mute button on the phone to block out some of the words, so all her mum heard was, "Help! It's an emergency, call police"

### Page 63

He stood on a block of ice and waited for it to melt

### Page 64

**Top:** He waits for night, and exits through the first door

### Page 65

**Top:** It was a convertible car, with the roof down

### Page 66

**Top:** He is cleaning windows on the inside of the building
**Bottom:** They are a cricket team

### Page 67

**Top:** The woman thought that if the man really thought it was his room, he wouldn't have knocked, and would have used his room key to open the door instead

**Page 68**

   **Top:** The postman did it because the post doesn't get delivered on Sundays

   **Bottom:** He shot his own reflection in the mirror

**Page 69**

   **Top:** To see if the man would come to her sister's funeral

   **Bottom:** His neighbour was snoring loudly, so he phoned his neighbour to wake him up. This put an end to the snoring and enabled the man to fall asleep

**Page 70**

   The police didn't tell the man the exact location of the crime scene. The fact that he knew the location without being told, alerted the police to the fact that he was the killer.

## ANSWERS (QUICK-FIRE ROUND)

**Page 72**
 **Top:** None. Moses wasn't on the Ark, Noah was
 **Middle:** Bread
 **Bottom:** The word 'incorrectly'

**Page 73**
 **Top:** Hopefully you
 **Bottom:** There is no such thing as half a hole

**Page 74**
 Add a diagonal line to the first plus sign to turn it into a number 4, so that the sum changes from 5 + 5 + 5 into 545 + 5 = 550

**Page 75**
 The photograph is taken on the moon, so there shouldn't be another moon in the sky

**Page 76**
 **Top:** It will be midnight in 72 hours' time and therefore dark
 **Middle:** ICE
 **Bottom:** Beacuse you can't bury people who are still alive

**Page 77**
 **Top:** Water
 **Bottom:** The word 'the' is repeated twice in the instruction

**Page78**
 Remove the side and bottom matches from the left-hand block, the right side match from the middle block, and the top and bottom matches from the right-hand block to leave the following:

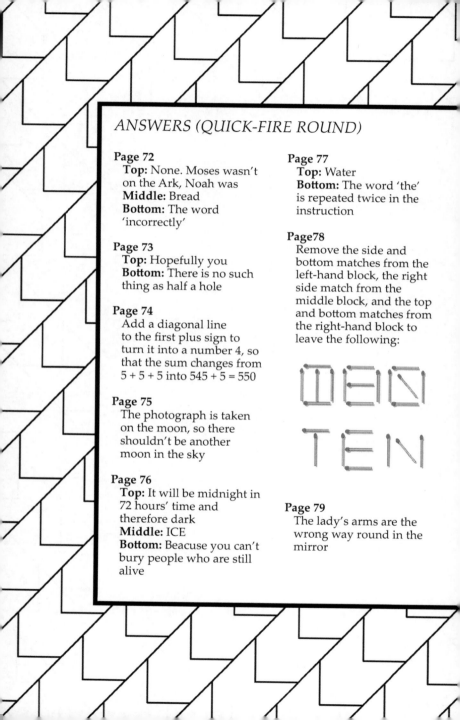

**Page 79**
 The lady's arms are the wrong way round in the mirror

## Page 80

**Top:** Stop imagining

**Middle:** There is no smoke because it is an electric train

**Bottom:** Roosters don't lay eggs

## Page 81

**Top:** SWIMS

**Middle:** Put a decimal point between the 2 and the 3 to make 2.3, which is less than 3 but more than 2

**Bottom:** Yesterday, today and tomorrow

## Page 82

**Top:** Zero

**Bottom:** There are no stairs as she lives in a bungalow

## Page 83

**Top:** E N T (Each letter represents the first letter of the written numbers: One, Two, Three, Four etc)

**Middle:** A 1p and a 2p. One of the coins is not a 2p, but the other is

**Bottom:** Mary

## Page 84

**Top:** 11 + 1 = 12

**Middle:** Add the letter G and it's gone

**Bottom:** That. (How do you spell THAT)

## Page 85

**Top:** Absolutely nothing. There are only 30 days in June, so June 31st doesn't exist

**Middle:** They weigh the same, one kilogram

**Bottom:** Albumen (the yolk is the yellow part)

## Page 86

**Top:** None, because the rest got scared and flew away

**Middle:** You don't bury survivors

**Bottom:** His car door